PART OF ME

PART OF ME

FRACTIONS AT REACH

QEONA HAMILTON-AGUILAR

Part of Me: Fractions at Reach © Copyright 2023 Qeona Hamilton

ISBN: 979-8-89109-143-6 (paperback)
ISBN: 979-8-89109-144-3 (ebook)
ISBN: 979-8-89109-108-5 (hardcover)

For more information, email authorqeona@gmail.com

This book is dedicated to a former student, A. A. . In 2013, we made a commitment to make our goals a reality.

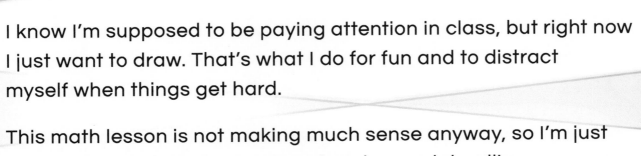

I know I'm supposed to be paying attention in class, but right now I just want to draw. That's what I do for fun and to distract myself when things get hard.

This math lesson is not making much sense anyway, so I'm just going to keep glancing up at my teacher and doodling in the page margins.

I hope it looks like I'm working, because if Mr. Ayala says, "KeAndre," with that sharp tone he has I'll be embarrassed all over again.

You might wonder what I'm drawing. Well, I'm just using my right hand to draw my left. I think a hand is one of the most convenient things to draw because it's always here, in front, or beside me.

4

Mr. Ayala announces, "In the next segment of our lesson, we will find equivalent fractions." Shaking my head, I think to myself, "I don't even know what he talkin' about."

Mr. Ayala starts referring to units, parts, and wholes, drawing square tiles and random circles on the whiteboard. They look so boring. Maybe he should use sandwiches, pizza, or pie as examples instead.

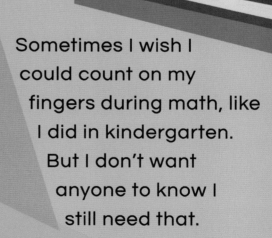

Sometimes I wish I could count on my fingers during math, like I did in kindergarten. But I don't want anyone to know I still need that.

When I lift my head and glance around the classroom,
I can tell by the confused faces that I'm not the only
one who doesn't get it. I start wondering...

Part of me says concentrate,
Pay attention and participate.

Part of me wants to try my best,
Put my skills to
the test.

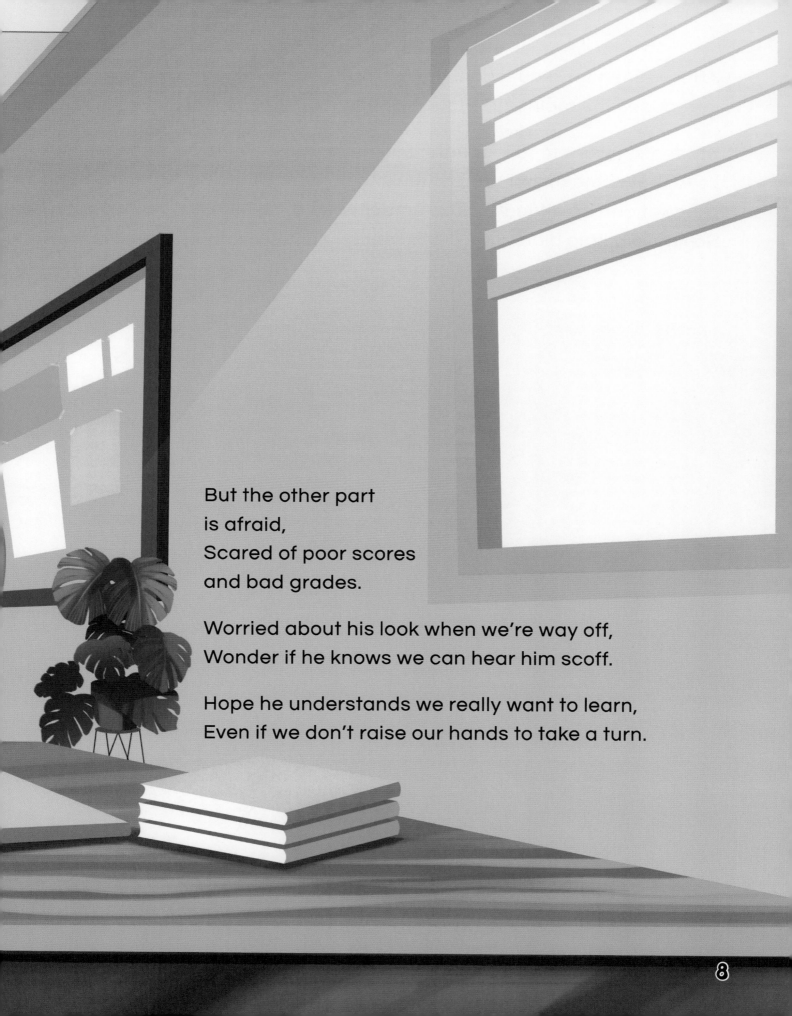

But the other part
is afraid,
Scared of poor scores
and bad grades.

Worried about his look when we're way off,
Wonder if he knows we can hear him scoff.

Hope he understands we really want to learn,
Even if we don't raise our hands to take a turn.

After waiting for a question, Mr. Ayala
introduces the main part of the lesson:

Students, I want to talk about fractions and
I see that some of you are just looking at your hands.
I know it can be difficult to remember what a fraction is,
So I have a little plan.

Notice, children, you have two hands
with five fingers on each.
Choose one hand to focus on for now
And listen close to what I teach!

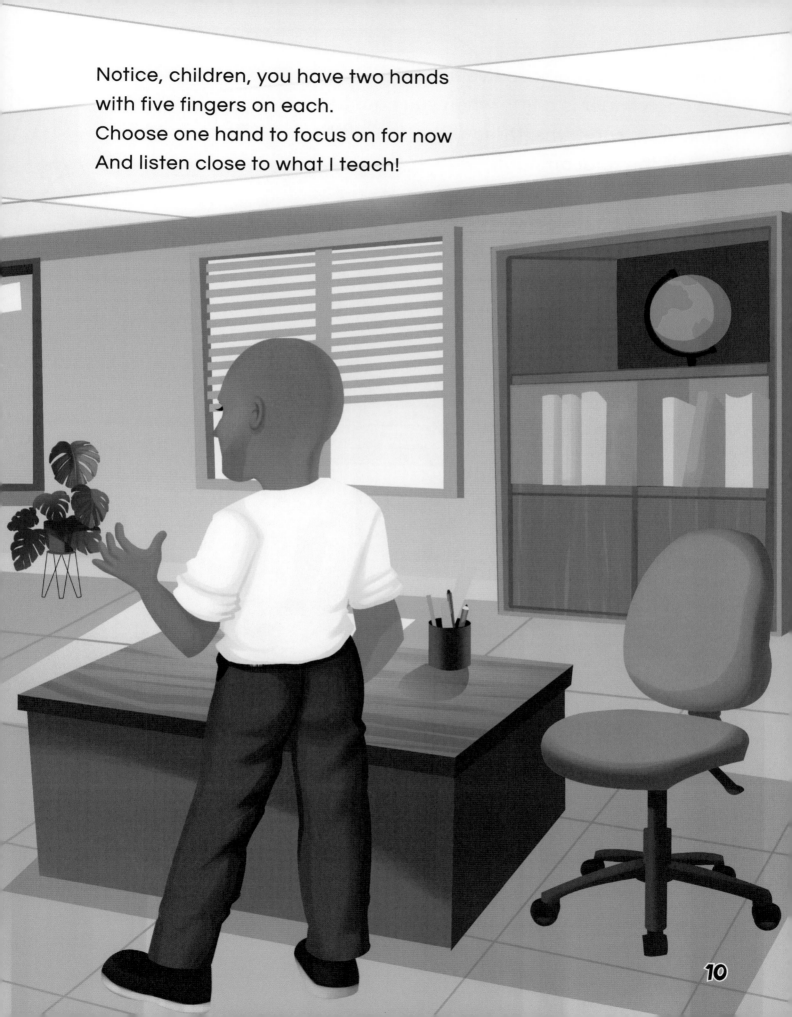

On one hand you have five fingers.
So each finger is a fifth when you count:
One-fifth, two-fifths, three-fifths, four-fifths, five-fifths.
That's the total amount.

One of your fingers is called a thumb.
Let's try putting one thumb down.
What fraction of your fingers are up?
Four-fifths fingers! Now you're coming around!

To practice more, show the symbol for peace. Two-fifths of our fingers make the sign. Three fingers down and the other two up. You're understanding fractions just fine.

Now look at both hands: they make two wholes.
Each finger is still one-fifth.
Count each finger on both hands.
Ten-fifths fingers is quite a gift.

$$+ \frac{1}{5} + \frac{1}{5} + \frac{1}{5} + \frac{1}{5} + \frac{1}{5} + \frac{1}{5} = \frac{10}{5} = 2$$

$$\frac{5}{5} + \frac{5}{5} = \frac{10}{5} = 2$$

If you take ten-fifths and
divide them in half
You're back to the original plan.
But now you know that
five-fifths plus five-fifths
Equals two whole hands.

Math involves the study of patterns.
Many arrangements tend to repeat.
Keep it going when you get home.
Practice fractions using your toes and feet!

Look at all your other digits
By removing your socks and shoes.
There are five toes on each foot
So apply the same mathematical rules.

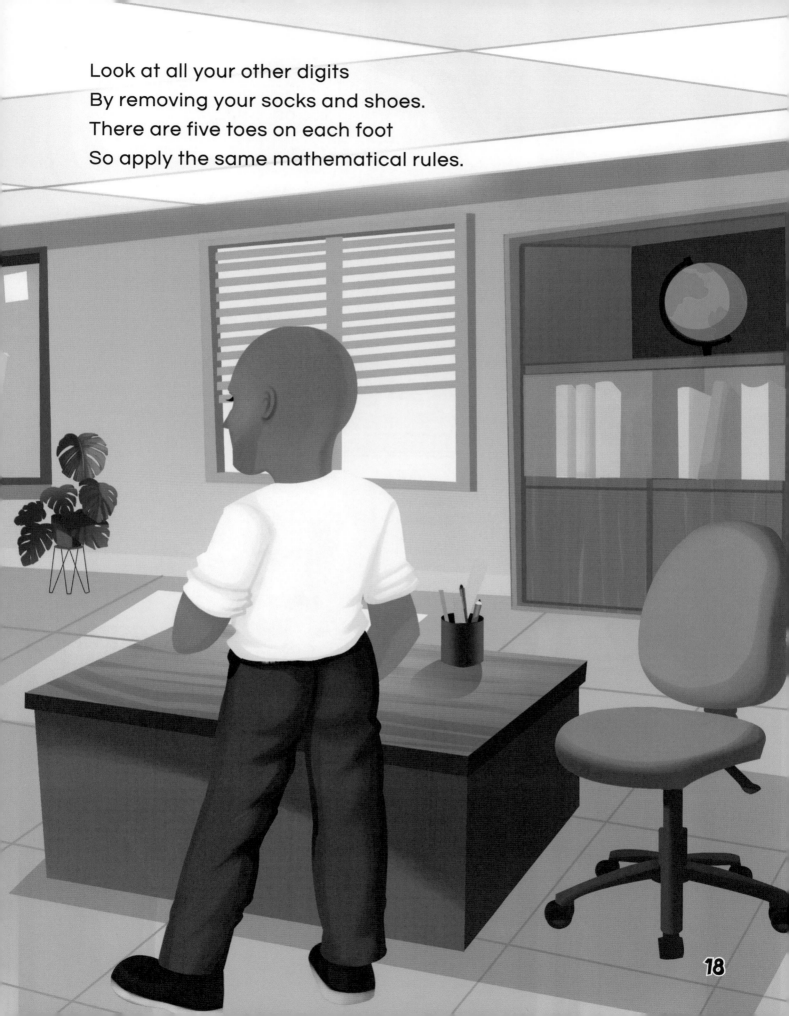

Notice, children, you have two feet
with five toes on each.
Choose one foot to focus on for now
And listen close to what I teach!

On one foot you have five toes,
So each toe is a fifth when
you count:
One-fifth, two-fifths, three-
fifths, four-fifths, five-fifths.
That's the total amount.

What fraction of one foot is equal to toes?
If you say five-fifths, you're on a roll!
One-fifth plus one-fifth plus one-fifth plus one-fifth
plus one-fifth is five-fifths.
And having all five of five is a whole!

Now look at both feet: they make two wholes.
Each toe is still one-fifth.
Count each toe on both of your feet.
Ten-fifths toes is quite a gift.

If you take ten-fifths and divide them in half
You're back to the original feat,
But now you know that five-fifths plus five-fifths
Equals two whole feet.

Look at the parts of your body
and you'll soon discover
There are many ways to understand fractions
and strategies to uncover.

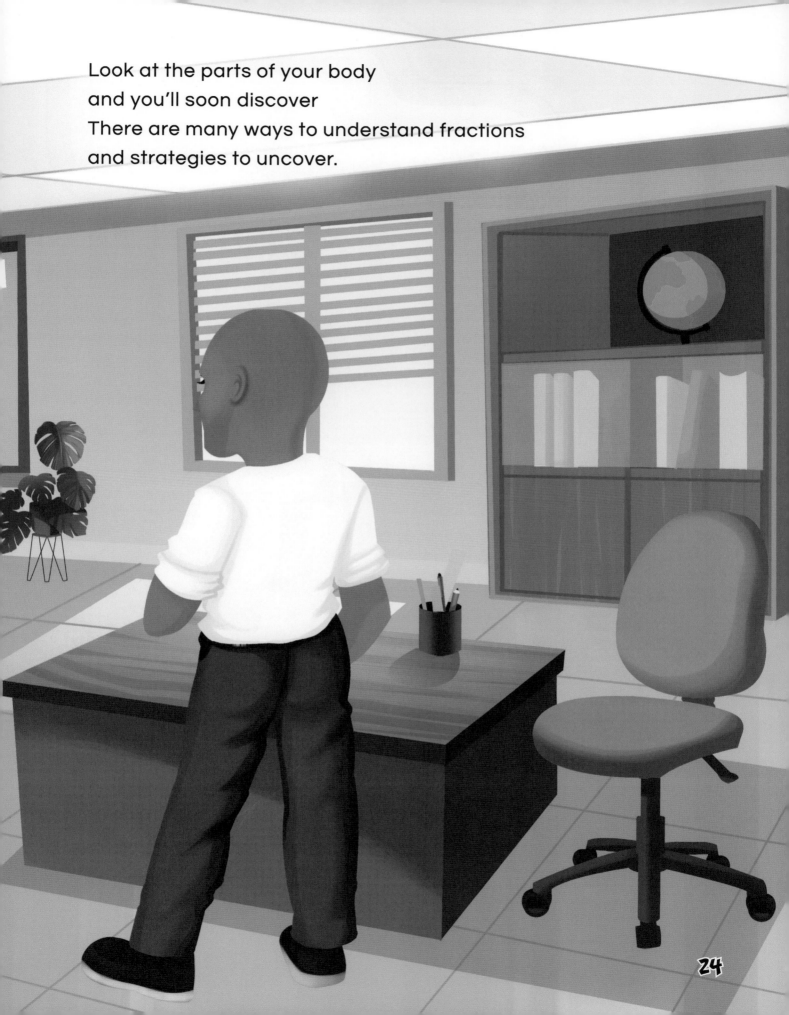

As Mr. Ayala concludes his rap, I realize I'm not drawing anymore. I put down my pencil so I could use my hands to understand fractions through his rhymes! My teacher knows exactly what to do to get through to us.

On the whole, Mr. Ayala breaks it down! "I wonder how he did dat," I thought. So, I raise my hand and he calls on me, "Yes, Dre?" "Mr. Ayala," I ask, "why did you create a rap about fractions?"

Part of me doubts if I'll ever be good at math. But another part of me is confident that I will do my best to use what I have to understand it. Especially with Mr. Ayala's help.

Mr. Ayala explains that he knows many of us love to draw, so he made a plan to teach us to use our hands as tools. He hears us singing and rapping at lunch, which means we relate to music. He puts those passions together to make it connect for us and it works!

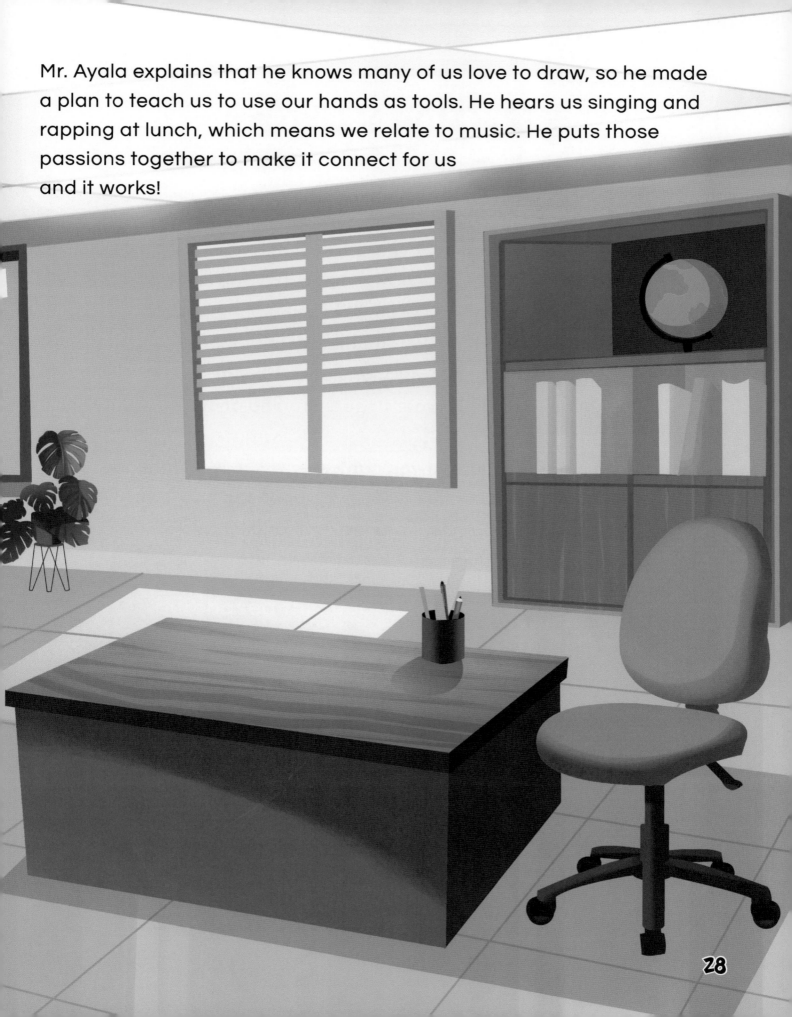

FRACTION ACTIVITIES FOR PARTS OF YOU!

Look at one of your hands.

What fraction of your hand is a thumb?

Flex your thumb. How many parts do you see?

Those parts of your finger are called phalanges.

What fraction of your thumb are phalanges?

Flex your fingers. How many parts do you see?

What fraction of your fingers are phalanges?

There's a part of you that you can't see, which is your heart.

Your heart has four chambers: two upper and two lower.

The upper chambers are the right and left atria.

The lower chambers are the right and left ventricles.

What fraction represents each chamber of the heart?

What fraction of the heart does the upper chamber represent?

What fraction of the heart does the lower chamber represent?

Thank you to every family member,
friend, colleague and supporter.
I hope after reading this book, you come to love it and
want to share it with everyone: children, educators,
individuals, and families. Read it for enjoyment.
Help children make connections. Employ it as a
teaching tool. Peruse it for ideas. Let it inspire you
to think of more ways to support our children.

Your feedback is valuable!
Please head over to the website where you
purchased this book and leave a review.
Want to join my email list? Reach out to me at
authorqeona@gmail.com!

I appreciate your time. Thank you.

QEONA HAMILTON-AGUILAR is an educator at an elementary school she attended in Los Angeles, California. She was born and raised in a neighborhood called South Central L.A. Qeona believes that she represents her community and it represents her. "I am our students and they are me." In publishing this book, she hopes to validate home language, honor culture, and highlight the importance of differentiated instruction for every child. Qeona's love of education came from her mother. She enjoys working and playing with her husband, Oscar, and watching their children and grandchildren grow. They have a pet named Tina who is a red-eared slider turtle. Tina befriended a goldfish, who has since joined the family.

Printed in Great Britain
by Amazon